Little Town of Spirals

Cynthia Matyi

DEDICATION

In remembrance of the best mother-in-law in the world,
Marion Matyi, musician and kindergarten teacher.
– C. M.

Thanks to my husband Stephen Matyi
for his imagination, vision, perspective and support.

Many thanks to talented writer Joyce Keeshin,
for her artistic contribution, wisdom, faith and practical advice
during the creation of this story.

Thanks also to two wonderful resource people,
Kim Sommer and Denise Kisor for their help
with the concept for this book.

First Edition Published in 2008 by Celtic Designs and Music

Text and Illustations copyright 2008 by Cynthia R. Matyi Celtic Designs and Music

All illustrations are from oil paintings by Cynthia R. Matyi

Graphic Design by Zooland Cre8ive

Printing by SpringDot, Cincinnati, Ohio

Binding by John Galt Bindery, Dayton, Kentucky

ISBN # 978-1-60461-735-1
Library of Congress Control Number   2007908174

Summary: "Little Town of Spirals" invites us on a whimsical journey to a wonderful place where spirals can be found almost everywhere!

Cynthia Matyi Celtic Designs and Music
P.O. Box 9121
Cincinnati, Ohio 45209-0121

www.matyiart.com

In a little town
of spirals
somewhere...

All the people
have curly hair.

On sunny days,
flowers whirl
and blossom.

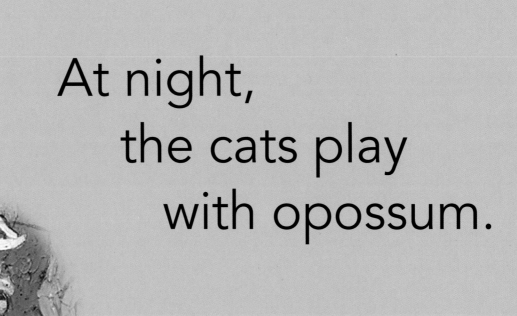

At night,
the cats play
with opossum.

The water circles
flowing down,
   and laughing rivers
   grace the town.

The farmers plow
in curvy ways,

while flocks of sheep
delight to graze,
around the windmills
like a maze.

The school is in
a round stone tower,

changing class
with every hour.

There is a band
whose sound
is round,

stirring spiral creatures
underground.

Their instruments
are proud and loud
for dancers spinning
in the crowd.

Father Night twirls stars
from his perch

as men in boats
go out to search.

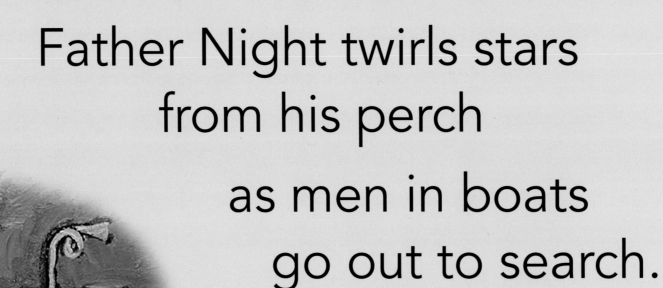

Mother Moon sends out
her golden threads,

spinning lovely dreams
in sleepy heads.

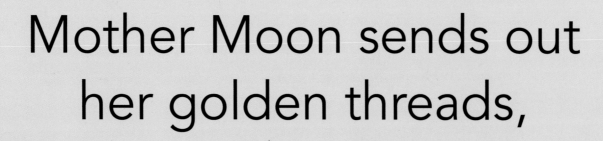

And now with one
last weary yawn...

sleep with spirals
'til the dawn.

CYNTHIA MATYI

Besides being a delight for the eyes and an intriguing place, "Little Town of Spirals" is an introduction to Celtic Art for the youngest of artists.

On a trip to Ireland in 2004, the author found herself showing a young boy of five how to draw spirals. Together they created a magical scene of a town where spirals rise from the chimneys, are present in the flowers and all manner of places. Since then she always asks students in her workshops "Where do we find spirals in nature?" The answers they come up with are amazing, opening the eyes of both teacher and students to patterns in the natural world.

"Little Town" is also a safe place for everyone, having the essence of both old and new, rural and sophisticated, simple but complex, comforting yet vaguely mysterious.

The colors supercede nature's expectations, with a tactile sense that invites a luxurious romp among the cabbages and curling waterfalls.

Watch for the bird with a brush to appear on each page. Repetition of shapes and characters encourage pattern recognition and the open-ended "non-plot" story encourages invention. And yes, cats do get along well with opossums.

Cindy Matyi spends her time painting Celtic art images as well as impressionistic "plein air" scenes. This book is a fusion of her styles into something unique and wonderful. Cindy loves giving Celtic Art classes to children. She is also a musician, gardener and community arts organizer.